THE BOOK
OF NUMBERS

An adventure
in
mathematics

THE BOOK OF NUMBERS

by
Dr Michael Thomson
with mathematics problems from
Ann Power

Illustrated by Bryony Jacklin

To Jonathan, with love.

The Book of Numbers
LD 610
ISBN 1-85503-113-2
© Text Michael Thomson
© Illustrations Bryony Jacklin
All rights reserved
First published 1991
LDA, Duke Street, Wisbech, Cambs. PE13 2AE, England.

READ THIS FIRST!

You are the star in this adventure story. When you read The Book of Numbers you will be on a quest for the missing Numbers of the World. You will visit a desert land. You will meet Counting Camel, the Number Cruncher and many other things.

As you go through the adventure you will be asked to do number tasks. You may need to get your answers checked by your teacher or your teacher may give you some answers so you can check yourself. As you go along you will be given clues and you will find things that will help you.

There is a very important piece of paper at the back of this book. It is your Equipment List. You can get this photocopied if you need to. In your adventure story you will find things to help you. You must write them down on your Equipment List. Write down the equipment number too so you can find it when you need it. If you do not have the right equipment you will have to go back to find it.

To begin the adventure start at the story number with **1** at the top. You will be told what to do next at the end of the story number. This could be to go on to another story number. You might be asked to choose where you want to go next or sometimes you will have to do a number task before you go on.

The Book of Numbers is the first of two books. The next one is called Number Quest. Now read on.

GOOD LUCK!

One day you go into a shop to buy some crisps. You find that you cannot work out how much money you are to get back from 50p. This is odd as you are good at working out money. It seems as if the numbers are not there anymore.

That night, as you lie in bed, you think about the shop. When you go to sleep you have a dream. Someone says, 'Yes! This is the one we have been looking for. The Numbers of the World are being taken away and soon no-one will be able to use them anymore'.

Someone else says, 'We must send Seekers to find the Message of the Numbers and save the Numbers of the World'.

You wake up with a start. You see a great task in front of you. It seems that something is moving in the Mists of Time. It will take from us all we know about numbers.

If you want to try and find out what is going on – go to **38**. If you do not want to help go to **11**.

You turn north and go to the Dead Tree. It has been dead for years and is now only a dried up husk. You are about to turn away when you hear a noise. It is a strange clicking noise. You look into the tree. There you see a very strange thing. It is a bit like an insect but it is the size of a small dog. It is almost square and has jointed legs. It has a long tongue which keeps shooting out. Its feet rub together making a clicking sound.

Counting Camel has stopped counting to look at this thing. When he starts counting again the creature opens its mouth. Huge teeth come out. Its legs whirl about. Its legs and tongue are feeding its teeth with all Camel's numbers. It is eating numbers! It is the Number Cruncher!

You turn to go. The Number Cruncher could crunch all your numbers. You will never be able to finish your task. As you go the Number Cruncher follows, crunching up Camel's numbers. You shout at it to stop. To your surprise it does stop. It looks up at you sadly. 'Oh all right! Come along!', you say. Write down the Number Cruncher on your Equipment List.

You head east to the Pyramid. As you go, you wonder where it will all end. You feel as if you are turning into a walking zoo for odd animals! Go to **58**.

3

You go to the Town. As you get close you can smell it! It smells of unwashed camels, cooking, spices and smoke. The people in the Town seem afraid. They keep looking at the Pyramid in the distance. They seem to think something might come from it. You try to ask them what the matter is. They will not tell you. They hurry away counting under their breath. They are trying to keep the numbers in their heads.

All at once a dark shadow comes over the Town. It is
a huge Dragon! It stares down on the Town with hate
in its eyes! It opens its mouth and breathes out fire.
Instead of burning you can feel all the numbers being
sucked out of the Town. The Number Cruncher starts
spitting out numbers to try and help. The Dragon looks
down and laughs. It seems to be in a hurry to get back
to the Pyramid. Just before it goes it looks back straight
at you! You hear it say in your mind, 'I have to go now.
If you think you will stop my Master, you are wrong.
We will meet again, Weak Human!'.

The Dragon flies off. The people come out from their
houses. They carry on their normal day. Today is market
day. Go to **4**.

4

You can:

- go on to the Pyramid - **111**
- visit the Bazaar (an eastern market) - **74**
- take a look at the Mosque (the church of the local people) - **17**

5

You see a trail that leads away from the Oasis. It goes through some tall sand dunes. You take the path. You see an odd shaped rock. It has a large hole in it. You can look inside the rock by going to **29** or you can go on - **30**.

6

You will have to get the Number Ten Bond. Perhaps the shape you saw before will help. You set out to look for it. After a while you see it again and chase after it - **84**.

7

That is not correct. Go back to **56** if you want to find the key.

8

You lie down under one of the trees. It is cool and peaceful. You fall asleep. When you wake up you feel rested. You eat some of the food that you have with you. Go to **67**.

You ask the woman to show you the key. 'First you must pay me, O Wise One', she says. Not again, you think, as you take out your money. The old woman asks you for some fractions of a pound. Do you have the Pound Chart? If not, go to the book shop (**104**) and then come back. Make a note of this story number if you are going to come back.

The Pound Chart will help you work out how much you should pay the old woman.

Write down:

a) $\frac{1}{4}$ of £1 _____

b) $\frac{1}{2}$ of £1 _____

c) $\frac{3}{4}$ of £1 _____

d) $\frac{1}{10}$ of £1 _____

e) $\frac{6}{10}$ of £1 _____

Now add up the five lots of money.

Write the total here _____

You should have £2.20 (220p). If you do not, check your work. When you have the correct answer go on to **26**.

Do you have the Columns of Ten and the Unit Cubes? If you do, read on. If you do not have them you will have to go back to get them from the Lizard – **79** for the Columns of Ten and **27** for the Unit Cubes. Then come back here. Make a note of this number if you are coming back.

You will need them to make a wall to shelter behind. You take them out and start to build with them to make the wall. Put them in the spaces for Tens and Units below. Then add them up. If your Units add to more than ten, don't forget to carry the extra Ten across to the Tens column.

	Tens	Units
a) 2 Tens and 3 Units	_____	_____
b) 1 Ten and 4 Units	_____	_____
c) 0 Tens and 5 Units	_____	_____
d) 2 Tens and 0 Units	_____	_____
e) 3 Tens and 3 Units	_____	_____

Your total should be 95. If it is, go to **69**. If you made a mistake, go to **35**.

11

What a shame! Your adventure has not even begun! Goodbye (or go to **38**)!

12

You ask for some gold. The Genie waves a hand, then he goes back into the lamp. You see some gold stones on the rock floor. You pick them up. It is 'Fool's Gold'! Fool's Gold looks like gold but it is not worth anything!

Now you can rub the lamp and buy another wish from the Genie - **15** - or go on to the Pyramid - **39**.

13

You rub the lamp on your sleeve. There is a puff of smoke and a loud bang! There, in front of you, is the Genie of the Number Lamp. 'What is your wish O Lord of the Numbers?', it says. You are about to make a wish when the Genie tells you that all wishes must be paid for! It seems that everyone is greedy for money in this part of the world!

First you need to add up your money. The Genie explains (he is keen to get hold of your money!):

£1.23 is £1 and 23 pence

£0.54 is £0 and 54 pence

If you have £1.67 and are given 85 pence, you can add them like this:

```
  £1.67
+ £0.85
-------
  £2.52    Now you have £2 and 52 pence (£2.52).
-------
```

The Genie tells you to add up your money so he can see how much to take. Do these sums:

a)   £1.35   b)   £1.54   c)   £2.38
   + £0.42   + £2.33   + £0.47

d)   £6.19   e)   £3.30   f)   £2.75
   + £2.42   + £4.76   + £3.97

Check your answers. If you were right, read on.
Correct and then read on if you made mistakes.

Now you will have to find out how much money you
have left to pay the Genie.

You may need the Scroll of Subtraction again.
Go back to **29** if you do. The Genie looks at all your
money and says, 'You can take away money like this':

If you have £1.00 and give the Genie 67p how much do
you have left?

We write:

    £1.00
— £0.67
   ‾‾‾‾‾‾‾‾

   ‾‾‾‾‾‾‾‾

First we go to the Pence column. Can we do 0 take
away 7? No. As we have no Tens in the Ten Pence
column we look at the £1 column. We change the
£1 coin into 10 Ten Pence coins.

$$
\begin{array}{r}
{}^{0}\ {}^{1}\\
£\cancel{1}.00\\
-\ £0.67\\
\hline
\\
\hline
\end{array}
$$

Now we can change 1 Ten Pence coin for 10 One Pence coins.

$$
\begin{array}{r}
9\\
{}^{0}\ \cancel{1}\ {}^{1}\\
£\cancel{1}.\cancel{0}0\\
-\ £0.67\\
\hline
\end{array}
$$

$$
\begin{array}{r}
9\\
{}^{0}\ \cancel{1}\ {}^{1}\\
£\cancel{1}.\cancel{0}0\\
-\ £0.67\\
\hline
3
\end{array}
$$

then 10 take away 7 is 3

$$
\begin{array}{r}
9\\
{}^{0}\ \cancel{1}\ {}^{1}\\
£\cancel{1}.\cancel{0}0\\
-\ £0.67\\
\hline
33
\end{array}
$$

and 9 take away 6 is 3

You can check your answer by adding again:

$$
\begin{array}{r}
£1.00\\
-\ £0.67\\
\hline
£0.33
\end{array}
\qquad
\begin{array}{r}
£0.67\\
+\ £0.33\\
\hline
£1.00
\end{array}
$$

Now do these:

Had	g)	£2.00	h)	£3.00	i)	£4.00
Spent		− £0.45		− £0.89		− £1.67

Had	j)	£5.00	k)	£10.00	l)	£2.00
Spent		− £2.13		− £ 4.85		− £1.97

Check your answers by the adding method. If you were correct go on to **15**.

14

You thank the boy but turn down the offer. No-one else comes to see you. After a while you leave the Village. Go to **93**.

15

You give some of your money to the Genie. He tells you that you have a wish. You can wish for:

- a Distance Chart - **41**
- some gold - **12**
- some jewels - **119**

The wind dies down. The ship is safe and you keep on sailing across the sea. At last you see some land ahead. At first it is just a thin strip far away. Then, as you come closer, you see a sandy shore. There is no green to be seen anywhere. You have come to a desert land! It is here that the Numbers of the World are going missing.

The ship comes in to land and you get off. It turns away and sails off on its own. You are on your own! You look around you. You can see some places that might help you:

- the Water Tower – go to **112**
- the Village – **32**
- the Old Caves – **71**
- the Stone Wall – **94**

Or you can start to go across the desert – **87**.

You go to look at the Mosque. This is the church of the Muslim faith. It has a dome and the walls are set with tiles. These make all kinds of shapes. You can look at these shapes more closely – **82** – or go back to **4** to choose again.

You thank the old man and take your ticket. You go to the harbour and find your ship. It is a big old sailing ship. You think that this is a bit strange, but you go up the gang plank.

At last the ship sets sail. There seems to be no crew on the ship. You are the only one on board. The ship goes faster and faster as if by magic.

Before you have time to think a strong wind begins to blow up. The wind is far too strong and rips the sails. The ship is in danger. The wind is now at Force 10 and is getting stronger. There is some strange power trying to stop you with a spell.

You can do nothing – go to **103**. Or, if you want to try to stop the wind blowing, go to **76**.

You come to an old shop tucked away in a corner of the Bazaar. An old woman waves to you. She asks you to come inside the shop. She says, 'I have the key you need to enter the Pyramid. You must choose wisely'.

If you want to stay and look at the key, go to **9**. If you think that it is nonsense you can leave the Bazaar – go to **4**.

You lay the ladders you have made across the quicksand. Now you can crawl over the sand to safety. Then you pull Camel out. The Number Cruncher helps you. It does not want to lose its food supply!

At last you are all safe. You rest for a while and then go on. You have not gone very far before you see a huge Lizard standing in your path. He is at least four feet long! All at once he runs at you hissing. A line of numbers jets out of his mouth. They hit you and burn like acid. He is one of the evil beasts sent to stop you saving the Numbers of the World. The numbers keep coming out at you, burning and stinging. Go to **22**.

21

Well, you were told that you needed it! You only have yourself to blame as you die in the desert, alone and in great pain!

What will you use to help you? Check your Equipment List and choose from:

- Multiplying Water - go to **73**
- the Number Cruncher - go to **61**
- Counting Camel - go to **114**
- Adder - go to **51**

If one or more of these is missing from your Equipment List you must have missed a place. Go back and check that you have visited:

- the Water Tower - **48**
- the Dead Tree - **2**
- the Village - **92**
- the Seer's Cave - **36**

23

The shopkeeper wants to trade with you. You can offer him:

- Counting Camel - go to **25**
- the Number Cruncher - **34**
- some Snake Serum - **88**
- the Treasure Map - **59**
- the Number Ten Bond - **121**

24

What?! Too low! Go back to **112** and check or you will die of thirst!

25

Camel is not pleased. The shopkeeper *is* pleased. What a good deal, he thinks to himself. Go back to **23** and think again!

You give the old woman the money. She shows you three keys. You can take one of them. If you take the gold key, go to **60**. If you take the old rusty iron key, go to **86**. If you take the new silver key, go to **106**.

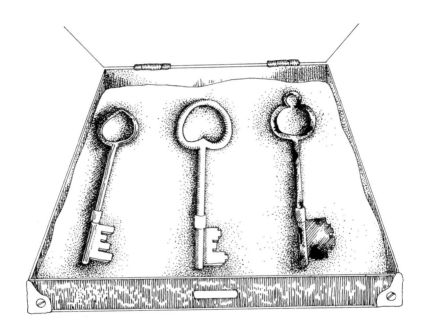

You follow the Lizard over a rise and down into a dip in the sand dunes. There you see a pile of stones. The Lizard has been hiding these here for a long time. He seems to want you to take some. You will need to decide which ones to take.

The stones are Columns of Ten and Unit Cubes. You have to collect up the Columns and the Cubes and write them in the table. If you see Columns of Ten put them under Tens. If you see Unit Cubes put them under Units. The first one has been done for you.

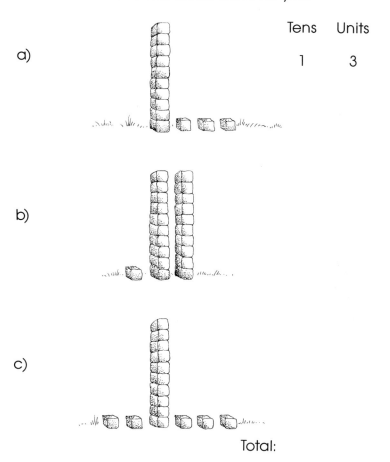

	Tens	Units
a)	1	3

b)

c)

Total:

Now add 23, that is 2 Tens and 3 Units to the total.

New total:

Your new total should be 72. If it is, go to **28**. If not, try again or get some help.

You take the Unit Cubes. Write them down on your Equipment List. You thank the Lizard. He seems to understand you. As you walk away he sits on top of the hill watching you. There seems to be a smile on its face. You wave and head for the Pyramid - **65**.

29

You look inside. There is something in there. It looks like a scroll. You reach in and take it out. It is very old but you can just read it. It is the Scroll of Subtraction. Write it down on your Equipment List.

You put the Scroll away and carry on down the path to **30**.

Scroll of Subtraction

To help you take away or subtract, you need to know what to do. Here is the Way, O Reader. Let us say you have the sum:

```
  TU
  67
− 18
  ──

  ──
```

This says 67 take away 18.

First we go to the Units (the right-hand column called U). What is 7 take away 8? As 7 is smaller than 8 we have to look at the Tens column (the left-hand column called T). The number 6 is in the Tens column. If we take one Ten, we are left with 5 Tens. We write the one Ten we have taken next to the 7 to make 17 Units, like this:

```
  TU
  5 1
  ̸67
− 18
  ──

  ──
```

So now we have 17 take away 8 (17 − 8).

```
  TU
  5 1
  ̸67
− 18
  ──
   9
  ──
```
$17 - 8 = 9$

Now we go to the Tens

```
  TU
  5 1
  ̸67
− 18
  ──
  49
  ──
```
5 take away 1 is 4. So we have 4 Tens and 9 Units.

Get some help if this does not make sense to you! You can look at the Scroll of Subtraction at any time. Make a note of the story number.

As you go down the path it splits into four smaller paths. They have some numbers on them. You need to follow each path, filling in the missing numbers as you go. You will need the Box of Signs to remind you what the signs on the paths mean. If you haven't got the Box of Signs, go back to **70** to get it and then come back here. Make a note of this story number if you are going to come back. *56*

Follow the four paths and write in the missing numbers. Do what the signs tell you.

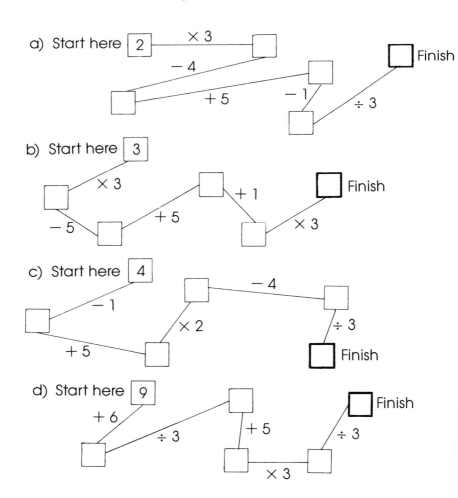

a) Start here [2] — × 3 — [ ]   [ ] Finish
    − 4
    [ ]   + 5   − 1   ÷ 3
    [ ]

b) Start here [3]
    [ ] × 3   [ ] + 1   [ ] Finish
    − 5 [ ] + 5   [ ] × 3

c) Start here [4]
    [ ] − 1   [ ] − 4   [ ]
    + 5   × 2   ÷ 3
    [ ]   [ ] Finish

d) Start here [9]
    + 6   [ ] + 5   [ ] Finish
    [ ] ÷ 3   [ ] × 3 [ ] ÷ 3

Now go to **37** to check your answers.

31

You find a new path. It takes you out of the Oasis. In the distance you see the Pyramid. You head towards it again. The sun burns down on your head. You keep having to drink water. The dried bones of dead animals are lying around. What a bleak place this is!

You find that it becomes harder and harder to walk. You fall down. You try to get to your feet. The sand slips and slides around you. At last you find your feet. You see a rocky part of the desert just ahead. You can go and rest under an overhanging rock that you see - **33** - or hurry on to **110**.

32

A little way inland you see the Village. The houses in the Village are made of mud and straw which has baked hard and dry in the sun. You walk slowly up to the Village (it's too hot to go quickly!). You go into the sandy streets. Some people dressed in long black robes stare out of the dark houses. Most hide away.

You notice a strong smell. It comes from the end of the Village where you find some camels! They are in large pens and are for sale. A boy of about 12 comes out of a house to meet you. 'Do you want to buy a camel?', he asks with a grin on his face.

One of the camels looks at you and sneers. It also spits on the ground. (Camels are fond of doing this sort of thing.)

If you want to buy a camel, go to **92**. If you do not, go to **14**.

You need to rest in the shade. There is more shade under some parts of the rock than others. You will have to choose which part has most shade. You can do this by looking at the shapes of the rock. How much of each shape is shaded? Write down the fraction next to each shape:

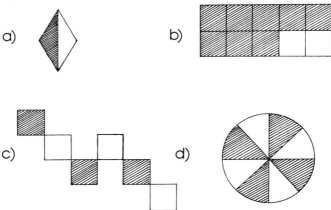

a) b) c) d)

Hint: count up all the parts in each shape (Counting Camel can help!). Then count up the shaded parts. If you counted four parts and three of these were shaded the fraction is $\frac{3}{4}$.

Which shape has the biggest fraction (most shade)?

Write your answer here _____ Now go to **47**.

34

What! Who will help you when you meet the Dragon again?! Back to **23** and think again!

35

You are too slow. The sand is cutting into you. You will be covered with sand. Go back to **10** and try again.

The total should be 114. If you were wrong the snakes eat you up (after biting you all over of course). If you were right the old man makes a sound like a hiss. All the snakes vanish apart from one. This snake has a diamond shape on its back. It climbs up your leg to your neck and drapes itself around your shoulders. You hear a hissing purr in your ear. The snake is happy.

'This is Adder', the Seer says. 'It will help you in time of need, O Chosen One, and be your friend.' The Seer also gives you a flask of anti-adder Serum (anti-poison). Write down Adder and Snake Serum on your Equipment List.

You ask the Seer to tell you if you will be able to save the Numbers of the World. He says that the Mists of Time are too cloudy. He tells you that an evil force is trying to take all the Numbers of the World. You may be the only one to save them. Then he gives you a Treasure Map. Write it on your Equipment List.

Now you can go to:

- the Village – **32**
- the Stone Wall – **94**
- the Water Tower – **112**

Or you can start across the desert – **87**.

You have found four numbers in the four 'Finish' boxes. They should be:

a) 2

b) 30

c) 4

d) 10

If you were not correct try again or get some help.

Hint: any ÷ or × can be done with the help of the 3 times table (go to **61** to look at it).

When you have done it correctly you can look at some other parts of the Oasis by going to **67**. If you want to leave the Oasis go to **31**.

You get out of bed. You see that an atlas has fallen open. It shows a page with some maps. You will have to find a ship to go across the sea! You go down to the harbour. The streets are dark. A strange light can be seen in the sky. Something is happening tonight!

Out of the corner of your eye you see a black shape. It runs down the road towards the sea. If you want to you can run after the shape - go to **84** - or you can carry on to the harbour - **63**.

You leave the lamp and walk off into the desert. After a while you come to some more rocks. You will have to find a way past the rocks. There are some paths. They twist and turn. Every way you look there are squares full of numbers.

You are in the Mazes of Numbers. You must get through the Mazes. Each time you step on a square you must add that number to your total before you can leave it. You get past the first Maze like this:

You go in at IN. Then you can only go across, up or down:

IN → [3] → [4] → [1]   1

2   8   [4]   9

7   [9] ← [6]   4

OUT = 27

3 + 4 + 1 + 4 + 6 + 9 = 27

In the next Maze, you must step on squares to make 50. Go in where it says IN and leave at OUT.

Hint: use the Number Ten Bonds.

IN → [10]   9   4   6   2   1   6

       3   1   8   2   7   8   5

       8   7   4   3   3   6   [4] → OUT = 50

       5   8   1   7   9   2   0

Keep trying until you find your way out. Then go to **53**.

You will need to get this right before you can go on.
You don't want to die here, all alone, in the desert! Go
back to where you were and have another go at the
numbers. You may need to get some help. Good luck!

You ask for a Distance Chart. 'A Wise Wish, O Master!',
the Genie says. 'I will grant you this, but I can give you
no more wishes.' He waves a hand and then goes back
into the lamp.

You see a chart on the ground. It is a Distance Chart.
It will help you find out how far to go. Write down
Distance Chart on your Equipment List.

The Distance Chart

The chart shows distances. It shows kilometres, metres
and centimetres. These are also written km, m and cm.
It also shows distances as fractions or parts of distances.
For example, $\frac{1}{4}$ kilometre is 250 metres.

100 centimetres = 1 metre				1,000 metres = 1 kilometre			
$\frac{10}{10}$	100 cm	1 m	$\frac{4}{4}$	$\frac{10}{10}$	1,000 m	1 km	$\frac{4}{4}$
$\frac{9}{10}$	90 cm			$\frac{9}{10}$	900 m		
$\frac{8}{10}$	80 cm	75 cm	$\frac{3}{4}$	$\frac{8}{10}$	800 m	750 m	$\frac{3}{4}$
$\frac{7}{10}$	70 cm			$\frac{7}{10}$	700 m		
$\frac{6}{10}$	60 cm			$\frac{6}{10}$	600 m		
$\frac{5}{10}$	50 cm	50 cm	$\frac{2}{4}$ $(\frac{1}{2})$	$\frac{5}{10}$	500 m	500 m	$\frac{2}{4}$ $(\frac{1}{2})$
$\frac{4}{10}$	40 cm			$\frac{4}{10}$	400 m		
$\frac{3}{10}$	30 cm	25 cm	$\frac{1}{4}$	$\frac{3}{10}$	300 m	250 m	$\frac{1}{4}$
$\frac{2}{10}$	20 cm			$\frac{2}{10}$	200 m		
$\frac{1}{10}$	10 cm			$\frac{1}{10}$	100 m		

Now answer these questions:

kilometres

a) How far is $\frac{1}{10}$ km? _____

b) How far is $\frac{7}{10}$ km? _____

c) What fraction of a kilometre is 500 m? _____

d) 750 m is _____ of a kilometre.

metres

e) How far is $\frac{1}{10}$ of a metre? _____

f) What fraction of a metre is 50 cm? _____

g) How far is $\frac{2}{10}$ of a metre? _____

h) 25 cm is _____ of a metre.

Check your answers. If you were correct you know you will be able to use the Distance Chart in the desert and you can go on to **39**. If you made mistakes get some help. When you get them all right go to **39**.

42

Not bad! The A tower added up to 30. But there is one with 31! Go back to **112** and check or you will have no water for the desert.

You look up. You see a tall man at the other side of the Oasis. He holds a sword in his hand. He is the Guardian of the Treasure. He can kill you with his magic sword. He sees you have the treasure. Now he wants you to give back some of the treasure. You will have to add up the money to see how much you can give him. To help you add it up, choose from:

- Multiplying Water and Snake Serum - go to **90**
- Adder and the Columns of Ten and Unit Cubes - **44**
- the Number Cruncher and Counting Camel - **101**

Adder starts to add up the money. You use the Tens and Units to help. If the Units come to more than ten you need to carry a Ten into the Tens column. This is shown by the little ₁ in the first sum.

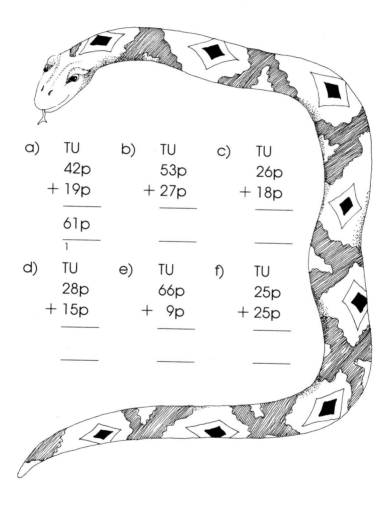

a) TU
   42p
+ 19p
──────
   61p
──────
₁

b) TU
   53p
+ 27p
──────

c) TU
   26p
+ 18p
──────

d) TU
   28p
+ 15p
──────

e) TU
   66p
+ 9p
──────

f) TU
   25p
+ 25p
──────

Get your answers checked. If you were correct, you can pay off the Guardian of the Treasure and carry on - **67**. If not try again.

You show the Number Ten Bond to the old man. 'All very well,' he says, 'but can you use it? To get a ticket you must be able to use the Number Ten Bonds.' Use your Number Ten Bond to write in the missing numbers and make up the tens.

$7 + \quad = 10$
$2 + \quad = 10$
$5 + \quad = 10$
$1 + \quad = 10$
$6 + \quad = 10$

Write down the numbers you used to make up the tens. You should have five numbers. Write them here:

_____ _____ _____ _____ _____

Now go to **49**.

You go down to the lake. You take a sip of water. It has a sharp taste but it is good to drink. You fill up one of your spare water bottles. You have found some Division Water. Write down Division Water on your Equipment List and then go to **67**.

The shape with the biggest fraction (most shade) was Shape B. It has $\frac{8}{10}$ or $\frac{4}{5}$. Go back to **33** and do it again or get some help if you got it wrong.

You sit down under the rock. It is cool here in the shade. You fall asleep for a while. You have a dream.

An evil twisted face mocks you. It says, 'How many numbers left now, O Foolish One?'. In your dream you see some sums. You know you must do them otherwise the evil face will take control of you.

Do you have the Scroll of Subtraction? Check your Equipment List. You might want to go·back to **29** to read the Scroll again.

Two of the sums, a) and g), have been done for you. You have to do the rest. You can check your answers by adding like this:

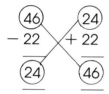 Your new answer is the same as the big number in the first sum.

In some of the sums you have to take a number from the Tens column. This happens in sum g) which has been done for you. Go back to the Scroll (**29**) if you have forgotten how to do this.

a)   46
    − 22
    ___
    24
    ___

b)   56
    − 13
    ___

    ___

c)   76
    − 24
    ___

    ___

d)   36
    − 10
    ___

    ___

e)   48
    − 18
    ___

    ___

f)   76
    − 20
    ___

    ___

g)   ⁴ ¹
    5̶0
    − 11
    ___
    39

h)   81
    − 16
    ___

    ___

i)   76   j)   25   k)   96   l)   47
    − 29   − 17   − 28   − 18
    ‾‾‾‾   ‾‾‾‾   ‾‾‾‾   ‾‾‾‾

    ‾‾‾‾   ‾‾‾‾   ‾‾‾‾   ‾‾‾‾

Check your answers. If you were correct, go to **50**. If not, try again until you are correct (check by adding).

48

Well done! You chose E tower – the right tower. You climb up the ladder to the top. There you find a big tub full of cool clear water! You also see a number of water flasks. You fill some with water to take with you across the desert. The water also has some magic. It can multiply things. This may be useful. Write down Multiplying Water on your Equipment List.

Now you can go to:

- the Village - **32**
- the Old Caves - **71**
- the Stone Wall - **94**

Or you can start across the desert - **87**.

49

You should have written 38594. This is the number of your ticket for the ship. If you did not write this number, go back to **45** and do it again until you get the right number. Then go to **18**.

The face fades away in your dream. You hear the words, 'You may have won this time but we shall meet again. Then it will not be so easy for you!'. You wake up with a start. You have a feeling that you will meet the face from your dream again but next time it will be for real.

Just as you are about to go on you see a glint in the sand. You take a closer look. It is a piece of metal sticking out. You brush the sand away. You see a strange looking lamp. You can either leave the lamp in the sand - **39** - or rub it against your sleeve - **13**.

Adder slides down from his perch. He starts adding the numbers together. This helps for a while. When the numbers are added they fall to the ground. But Adder is too slow. The numbers come from the Lizard faster and faster. Adder can't add quickly enough. Go to **22** and choose again.

You drive the snakes away. Adder puffs himself up as if he did it himself. He looks very pleased with himself. Camel just goes on counting.

You leave the rock and go on. After a while you see a single Dead Tree to the north. Then you see a shape far to the east. At first you think it is a mountain. Then you see that it is a distant Pyramid.

You can go north to the Dead Tree - **2** - or east to the Pyramid - **58**.

You walk out of the Mazes of Numbers and across the desert. Far in the distance you can see where you have come from. You have travelled a long way.

You need to decide where you want to go next. Do you have your Distance Chart? Check your Equipment List. If not, go back to **15**. If you do have it, you can work out how far you have come and how far you still have to go.

You will have to find out the answer to these questions before you can go on. All the distances are in kilometres.

a) How far is it from the Village to the Oasis?

b) How far is it from the landing place to the Oasis and then to the mountains?

Hint: add the two distances together.

c) How far is it halfway between the landing place and the Village?

d) What is the total distance from the Oasis to the mountains to the Pyramid to the landing place?

e) If you go 10 km from the Oasis to the landing place, how far have you gone - one quarter of the way?
one half?
three-quarters?

f) Which is the shortest route - from the Village to the Pyramid or from the mountains to the landing place?

g) Which route is longer (and by how many kilometres) - *landing place-Oasis-mountains* or *landing place-Village-mountains*?

Hint: your answer to f) will help you answer g).

Check all your answers. When they are all correct you can go on to **54**.

54

At last you find out which is the shortest way to the Pyramid. You see some smoke ahead. It is the cooking fire of a small town. You will need to go to the Town before you can go to the Pyramid - **3**.

55

Counting Camel is most upset. He digs in his feet and will not go on. You will have to let him race if you don't want to walk to the Pyramid. Go to **83**.

You look around the Oasis. You take out the Treasure Map that the Seer gave you. You see that it is marked with a cross. You find the spot in the Oasis. You dig and find an old chest. Next to the chest are some bags. They have money inside them. The bag with the most money has a key inside it. You can use this to open the chest.

Which bag has the most money? Add up the numbers in the coins.

Bag A   Bag B   Bag C   Bag D

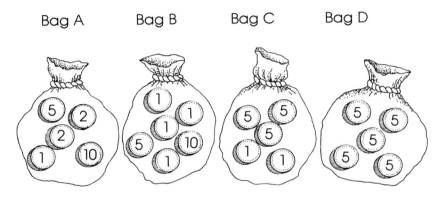

If you think it was Bag A, go to **7**. If you think it was Bag B or C, go to **117**. If you think it was Bag D, go to **70**.

The Imman says, 'Well done! You are the one I was hoping for! You may be able to beat the evil in the Pyramid. Take this Code to help you enter the Pyramid!'. He gives you a piece of ancient paper. It has the Code of the Pyramid written on it. Write down the Code of the Pyramid on your Equipment List. You can look at the Code at **115** if you want then come back. Go to **4** and choose again.

You go east to the Pyramid. It is a long way away. It will be some time before you reach it. Something tells you that you are on the right track but what about the Dead Tree? If you want to go back and check it out, go to **2**. Then you can come back.

All at once you find yourself sinking into the sand! You have walked into quicksand. Camel screams in fear. He thrashes around and gets deeper and deeper. You will have to pull him out. You can make some ladders out of numbers and then crawl across them.

Fill in the missing numbers on the ladders.

Ladder A   Ladder B

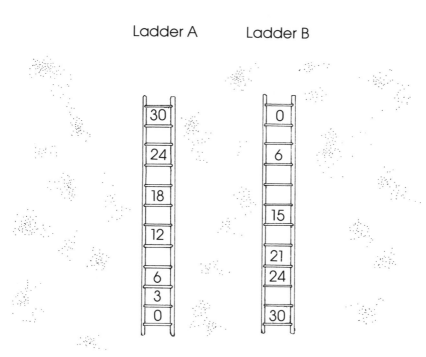

Check your answers. If you got it right, go to **20**. If you made a mistake, make a note of this story number and go to **40**.

You offer the Treasure Map. The shopkeeper looks at it. He seems to like it. Then you tell him that you have found the treasure so you know that the map is a good one! The shopkeeper is mad. 'So you try to sell me a map after you have taken the treasure, do you?'

You will have to do better than that! Go back to **23**.

60

You take the gold key. It is very grand. It must be worth a lot. The old woman smiles. 'Well, I suppose a gold key will be good for opening a Pyramid!'

Do you think it is? You can go back to **4** or choose again at **26**.

61

The Number Cruncher starts to crunch up the numbers coming from the Lizard. You notice that all the numbers are linked to three. You can make them into a 3 times table. As the numbers come out you can throw some Multiplying Water on them. The Number Cruncher then crunches them up.

You feed some numbers to the Number Cruncher. Now see if you can do these sums (the top two have already been done for you).

$4 \times 3 = 12$ $\qquad$ $7 \times 3 = 21$
$5 \times 3 =$ $\qquad$ $8 \times 3 =$
$6 \times 3 =$ $\qquad$ $11 \times 3 =$
$2 \times 3 =$ $\qquad$ $12 \times 3 =$
$9 \times 3 =$ $\qquad$ $1 \times 3 =$
$3 \times 3 =$ $\qquad$ $10 \times 3 =$

Check your answers. If you filled in all the spaces correctly, go to **78**. If not, make a note of this story number and go to **40**.

You have matched out the shapes! Well done! The Imman has been watching you. The Imman is the priest of the Mosque. He comes up to you. 'You seem to have a gift with numbers', he says. Will you stay and talk to the Imman at **95** or go on to the Pyramid at **111**?

You turn away from the shape and go to buy a ticket for the ship at the ticket office - **68**.

At last you get to the Pyramid. It is huge. It is made from thick stone and seems to rise out of the desert.

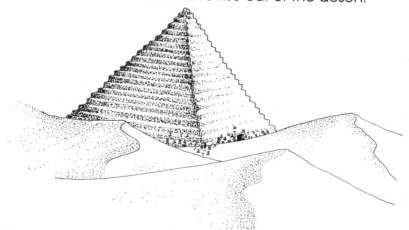

All is silent. You can see no way to get in at first. Then you notice that there are piles of old numbers all around the Pyramid. You can use:

- the Number Cruncher - **85**
- Counting Camel - **100**
- Adder - **107**

65

As you go across the desert the wind starts to blow. More wind spells are being used against you. A dust storm is in the air. You see a cloud of sand getting closer. You can either take no notice of the storm and go on to **97** or try and make a shelter - **10**.

66

You follow the Number Line. It goes to the Oasis. At the Oasis the grass is green and lush. There is a small lake with palm trees. It is cool and you stay there to rest. Go to **67**.

67

While you are at the Oasis you can:

- have a sleep - **8**
- collect some water from the lake - **46**
- look at the palm trees - **91**
- go along a strange path you see in the sand - **5** (if you have been down this path before and want to leave the Oasis, go to **31** but only if you really have been down the path!)
- look for treasure - **56**

68

You go down to the harbour. A ship is about to set sail. You need a ticket. You go into the ticket office. An old man sits at the desk. After a long time he looks up. Before he will give you a ticket he asks to see your Number Ten Bond. Check your Equipment List to see whether you have it. If not, go to **6**. If you do, go to **45**.

You make a big wall with the blocks. The wind is kept out. You are safe. The sand makes a crashing sound against the wall but you are safe behind it. At last the wind starts to die down.

You get up from behind the wall. The sand dunes have been moved about. Far away you can just see something. It looks green. Could it be an Oasis? You head that way.

After a while you realise that you are getting lost. Will you turn back to **120** or try to find the best way to go on - **108**?

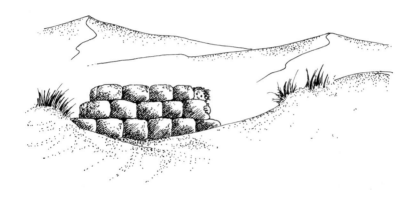

70

Bag D has the most money and the key is inside. You open the chest with the key. The chest is the Box of Signs. Write it on your Equipment List. You find some + signs to help you add. There are some − signs to help you subtract. You also find some × signs to help you multiply. So 2 × 3 = 6 or 2 bags with 3 sweets in each bag = 6 sweets. The ÷ sign tells you how to divide. So 6 ÷ 2 = 3 or if you have 6 sweets and 3 people they have 2 sweets each.

You may need the Box of Signs later. Now go to **43**.

Along the beach, a sandstone cliff rises up. You can see some caves in it. As you get closer you see a wisp of smoke coming out from the caves. Someone must live there. You go up to the caves slowly. You call out. There is no answer.

Slowly, you go into the caves. All at once a ragged old man leaps out at you with a shout. Your heart races madly as he glares at you. 'How dare you enter the Cave of the Seer?!', he cries. 'Do you not know that I see all? I knew you were coming and am ready with my power.'

With these words he points a bony finger at you. All at once you see that the floor is covered with millions of snakes. They writhe around and come towards you.

Quickly you tell the Seer about the dream you had and how you must save the Numbers of the World. The Seer says, 'All is dark in my dreams. If you are the Chosen One you must prove yourself. Fill in the missing numbers and we shall see what we shall see'.

a) 1 2 3 __ 5 6 7 8 9 10

b) 10 9 8 __ 6 5 4 3 2 1

c) 2 4 6 __ 10

d) 10 20 30 40 50 60 __ 80 90 100

e) 5 10 15 20 __ 30 35 40 45 50

Now add up the five missing numbers you have written in the spaces.

Write the total here _____ Go to **36**.

72

Counting Camel is given some dates to eat as a prize. You are given a small bag of money. If you want to spend some of the money in the Bazaar go on to **75**. If not, go back to **4**.

73

You splash Multiplying Water on your burns. You hope to cool yourself. The Water multiplies the burning numbers. It makes it worse. Go to **22** and choose again.

You go into the Bazaar. It is full of things to buy. It is also full of people. They push and shove you in all directions. You come to a large square. People are standing around the edge. It looks like a camel race is about to begin! Counting Camel looks at you. Will you let him join in the race? You can either go to **83** for the race or to **55** if you want to stay in the Bazaar.

75

You go on to the Bazaar. You see all kinds of things to buy - fruit, carpets, rice, brass, jewels and most things you can think of. You can look at a shop selling books and papers - **104** - or a shop selling keys - **19**.

76

The wind is at Force 10. What can you do to make it less than 10? You remember your Number Ten Bond. This time take numbers away from 10.

Fill in the missing numbers:

10 — $\boxed{}$ = 7

10 — $\boxed{}$ = 4

10 — $\boxed{}$ = 5

10 — $\boxed{}$ = 1

10 — $\boxed{}$ = 8

Check your answers. If you got all five right go to **16**.
If you made a mistake go to **103**.

77

The Pound Chart shows fractions of a pound.
Remember 100p = £1.

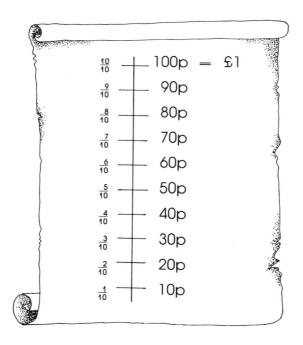

All at once the Lizard stops spitting out the burning numbers. He looks happy. He must have been under a spell to poison all the numbers. He turns to go. Then he looks back at you. Will you follow him – **27** – or go on to the Pyramid – **65**?

You should have found that Wall D had the highest total. It should have come to 24. (Go back to **94** to check if you want.)

You climb over Wall D. You find some columns. They are the Columns of Ten. You may need these later. Write down Columns of Ten on your Equipment List.

Now you can go to:

- the Village – **32**
- the Old Caves – **71**
- the Water Tower – **112**

Or you can start across the desert – **87**.

You take the Pound Chart. You can look at it again at **77** when you need to. Write it down on your Equipment List. Now go to **19**.

The Imman says 'Oh dear! You do not seem to be the one I hoped for. You do not see the need to save the numbers.'

Unless you can do your answers to the signs again and learn their meanings your Quest ends here.

You take a close look at the shapes. Match the shape with the fraction. The first one has been done for you.

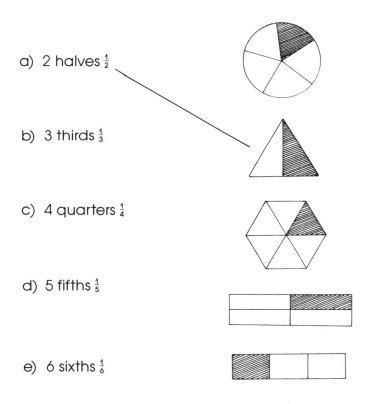

a) 2 halves $\frac{1}{2}$

b) 3 thirds $\frac{1}{3}$

c) 4 quarters $\frac{1}{4}$

d) 5 fifths $\frac{1}{5}$

e) 6 sixths $\frac{1}{6}$

Check your answers. If you were correct go on to **62**. If not try again and then go on.

83

You let Counting Camel join one of the racing teams. He does not seem to be very sporting. He spits at the other camels and kicks out at them! The camels race around the square kicking up dust.

Each of the two teams runs four races. The camels get points depending on whether they come first or second. These are the points for the four races:

	Counting Camel's team	The other team
Race A	32 points	39 points
Race B	40 points	14 points
Race C	26 points	23 points
Race D	25 points	17 points

a) Which race did Counting Camel's team score the most points for?

b) Which race did the other team score the fewest points for?

c) Which team scored the most total points and by how much?

d) How many more points does the other team need to add to its worst score to get the same as Counting Camel's team's best score?

Check your answers. When they are all correct you can go to **72** to collect Counting Camel's prize!

84

You chase the black shape down the road. It is a man running. He is very fast. You have 20 seconds to catch him. Count up to 20. Then count backwards from 20 down to zero. If you can do both in under 25 seconds go to **89**. If not, keep trying until you can do it!

85

The Number Cruncher starts to suck the numbers up and crunch them. After a short time the numbers clear away and you can see a door. It is set in the side of the Pyramid. There is a keyhole in the door. Do you have a key? If you do, go to **102**. If not, you will have to go back to **19** to get one.

86

You take the old rusty iron key. Write it on your Equipment List. The old woman smiles. Go to **4**.

87

It is time to look for the evil force that is taking away the numbers. You set out across the desert. Check your Equipment List to see if you have:

- the Number Ten Bond
- Counting Camel
- the Multiplying Water
- the Columns of Ten
- Adder
- the Snake Serum
- the Treasure Map

If any of these are missing from your Equipment List you can go back and get them - **16**.

If you have all the equipment or do not want to go back, go to **99**.

88

You give the shopkeeper some Snake Serum. You can spare it and it is a fair trade. Go to **80**.

89

At last you catch up with the man. He turns to you. 'Good evening', he says. 'My name is Bond – Number Bond. I am a secret agent and I can help you.' He gives you a piece of paper and runs off. 'Don't forget to eat the paper when you have read it!', he calls out.

If you want to read the paper, go to **96**. If you still want to buy your ticket, go to **68**.

The Multiplying Water makes some of the money grow, but you still do not know how much to give the Guardian of the Treasure. The Snake Serum does nothing. Go to **43** and choose again.

You walk over to one of the palm trees. You feel as if someone is watching you. You shake off the feeling and look up. The palm trees are full of coconuts! The coconuts are in sets of ten. If only you could get some! You need to take a few coconuts away from the trees.

You can use your Number Ten Bond or the Number Line at **108** to help you do these take away (subtraction) sums. The top two have been done for you.

$10 - 7 = 3$ $10 - 0 = 10$
$10 - 2 =$ $10 - 8 =$
$10 - 5 =$ $10 - 3 =$
$10 - 9 =$ $10 - 4 =$
$10 - 6 =$ $10 - 1 =$

Now you can check you answers. If you were correct, you can take some coconuts. If not, they fall on your head! Now go to **67**.

You have some money with you but the boy sets you a task before you can buy a camel from him. Some of the camels have one hump and others have two or a pair of humps. You must buy a two-humped camel. The boy says you must count up how many pairs there are before you can buy a camel.

How many pairs are there? Write your answers on the lines.

Pairs of eyes

_____

Pair of boots

_____

Pairs of lizards

_____

Pairs of humps

_____

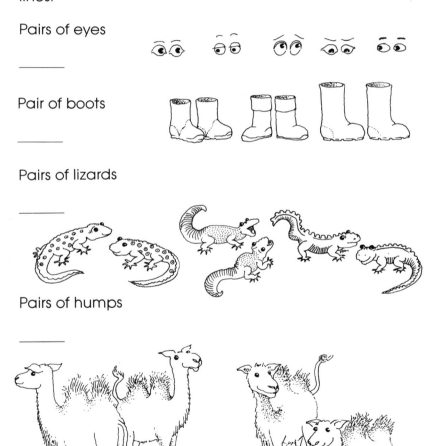

When you have counted the pairs of humps correctly the boy agrees to sell you a two-humped camel. He gives you a sulky looking beast. The boy tells you that this camel can count! You hope this is true. It might help you later. Write down Counting Camel on your Equipment List. Then go to **93**.

93

You can go to:

- the Water Tower - **112**
- the Old Caves - **71**
- the Stone Wall - **94**
- back to the Village - **32**

Or you can start across the desert - **87**.

A little way from the Village you see a Stone Wall. The wall does not seem to do anything. It just sits there in the middle of the desert. You go and take a look. The wall is really four walls next to each other. They are quite high. There are some handholds. You need to climb over the highest wall.

To climb them you have to add the next door bricks and put the total above them. Look at Wall A. Some of the counting has been done for you. The 4 brick has been added to the next door 3 brick. This gives 7. The number 7 has been written in the brick above. Then the 3 brick has been added to the 2 brick above. The next stage is climbing Wall A is to add the 7 brick and the 5 brick. This will give the total for the top brick.

Which wall has the biggest total?

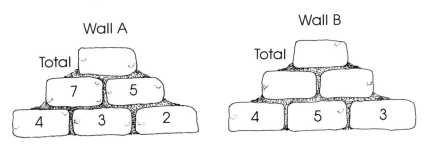

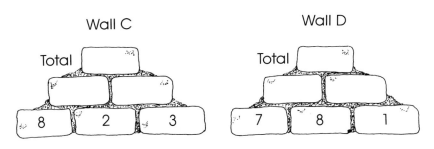

Now go to **79**.

The Imman tells you that an evil force has come from the Pyramid. It sends out the Dragon to take numbers from people. It is also taking the Gift of Mathematics from the world. He tells you that he has a Code that will let you into the Pyramid. First you have to prove you know what these signs mean. Write down your answer next to each one.

$+$

$-$

$\times$

$\div$

If you were correct, go to **57**. If not, go to **81**.

You open the paper (don't eat it!). Inside you find:

The Number Ten Bond

You can make 10 by using these number bonds:

1 + 9   2 + 8   3 + 7   4 + 6   5 + 5

6 + 4   7 + 3   8 + 2   9 + 1

Remember this well, O Seeker! You will need it soon!

Write down Number Ten Bond on your Equipment List. Now you can go to the ticket office - **68**.

Camel looks at you. He thinks you are mad to go on. Adder hides away. The dust storm starts. The sand cuts into your face. You are blown off your feet. You will have to find shelter or you will be buried in sand. Go to **10**.

98

You will have to go back and get it. Try the Imman at the Mosque - **17** or **95** if you went to **17** before.

99

The sun is baking hot as you set off across the desert. Counting Camel lurches along and you find it hard to hang on. The up and down of his back is making you feel sick. Counting Camel talks under his breath all the time. He is counting. He counts up to 1,000 and then down again, on and on and on.

You get off Camel's back to take a rest before he drives you mad. You sit on a large rock and take a sip of water. Camel says, 'One, two, three, one, two, three, one, two, three'. Over and over again. What an animal!

Just as you are plotting ways to stop Camel counting you notice two snakes by your hand. They have been sunning themselves on the rock. Adder rears up from around you to hiss but the snakes are too quick. One bites you on the arm. You can feel its venom (poison).

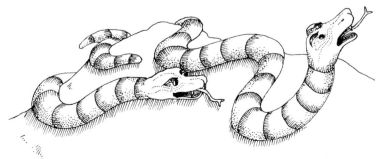

You will need to use the Snake Serum quickly. Check your Equipment List. If you have the Serum go to **116**. If not, go to **21**.

100

Camel counts them all up. They come to 345,567. Now what? Go back to **64** and choose again.

101

Counting Camel starts to crunch but it takes too long. The Guardian of the Treasure is waiting. Then the Number Cruncher eats the money. Try again at **43**.

102

If you have the gold or silver key, go to **109**. If you have the old rusty key, go to **105**.

103

Oh dear! The wind rises to a screaming force. It rips the sails off the mast. The ship is blown on to the reef. The hull is smashed and the ship sinks. You can cling to a bit of drift wood and let the tide take you back to the harbour - **68**.

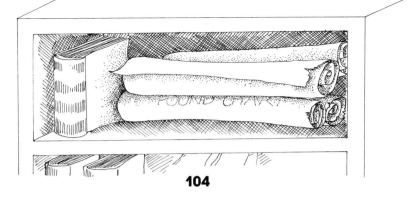

104

You go into the shop selling books and papers. You see a scroll marked the Pound Chart. You can buy it at **23** or you can go to the key shop at **9**.

105

You try the key in the lock. It fits! It is very stiff. It takes a lot of turning and twisting. Then at last the lock turns over. You push the door open. Inside is a second door! You see some numbers on the door. Do you still have the Code of the Pyramid? If you do, go to **113**. If not, go to **98**.

106

You take the silver key. The old woman smiles and says, 'Yes. I have just made that key'.

You wonder if a new key will fit an old Pyramid. You can go back and choose again - **26** - or go back to **4**.

107

Adder adds the numbers up. They come to 345,567. Now what? Go back to **64** and choose again.

A Number Line shows you the way to the Oasis. It can help you take away (subtract). Here is a Number Line:

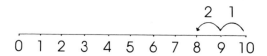

In this Number Line the sum 10 − 2 has been done. Start at the 10 and go back two places. You will arrive at 8!

Do these sums using the Number Line:

10 − 3 =   10 − 8 =
10 − 6 =   10 − 2 =
10 − 9 =   10 − 4 =

Now add the answers together. You should get 28. If you were correct, go to **66**. If not, you will have to try again.

Oh dear! You have the wrong key. You need an old one for an old Pyramid. Go back and choose again at **9**.

You go on. You are so tired. The sun drains you. You will have to rest! Go to **33**.

You leave the Town. You have a long way to go. You camp for the night and then move on. Time is getting short. You need to get to the Pyramid very quickly. Look at these clocks. Link up the clock time to the correct time in the box (digital display). One has been done for you.

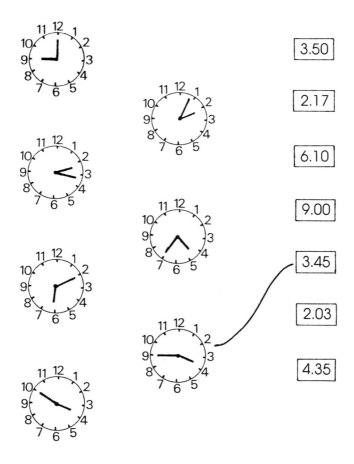

If you were correct, go on to **64**. If not, get help, do them again and move on to **64** when you have got them right.

You see five towers along the beach. Each tower is full of numbers. They are made of brown mud. There is a ladder up the side of each tower. At the top of one tower is a big tub of water. The tower with the water has the biggest number. You must find out which one it is.

Use your Number Ten Bond. Look at A tower. Find any Number Ten Bonds - like 6 + 4 or 8 + 2. Add all the tens in A tower. Then add any other numbers to your total. Do the same for each tower.

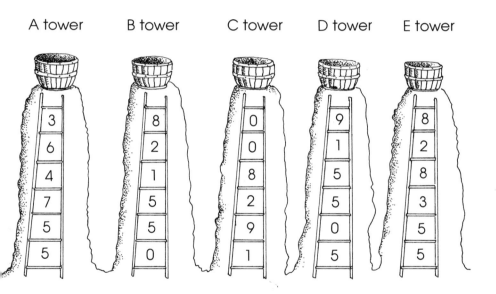

A tower   B tower   C tower   D tower   E tower

A tower	B tower	C tower	D tower	E tower
3	8	0	9	8
6	2	0	1	2
4	1	8	5	8
7	5	2	5	3
5	5	9	0	5
5	0	1	5	5

Write down the totals for each tower:

A =   B =   C =   D =   E =

Which tower has the biggest number? This is the one with the water in it. If you think it is A tower, go to **42**. If you think it is B tower, C tower or D tower, go to **24**. If you think it is E tower, go to **48**.

113

You take out the Code of the Pyramid. Go to **115** and use the Code to work out the Message of the Numbers.

11 09 16 03 22 13 09   10 22   10 24 09

04 17 06 18 13 07 21   22 05   01 19 13 12 09 06 02!

04 06 09 04 18 06 09   10 22   13 09 09 10   10 24 1

21 22 22 13!

114

Camel starts to count the numbers coming out of the Lizard's mouth. He does very well but the numbers come too fast and they are burning him. Go to **22** and choose again.

115

This is the Code you need for the Message of the Numbers.

a = 18   g = 14   m = 13   t = 10

b = 12   h = 24   n = 01   u = 19

c = 03   i = 07   o = 22   v = 23

d = 21   j = 08   p = 04   w = 11

e = 09   k = 25   q = 26   x = 15

f = 05   l = 16   r = 06   y = 17

s = 02   z = 20

Write down the Message of the Numbers below.

Now go to **118**.

You take out the Serum and drink some. It will stop the venom. Now you need to scare off the snakes or you will be bitten again. Drive them away by filling in the missing numbers on their backs.

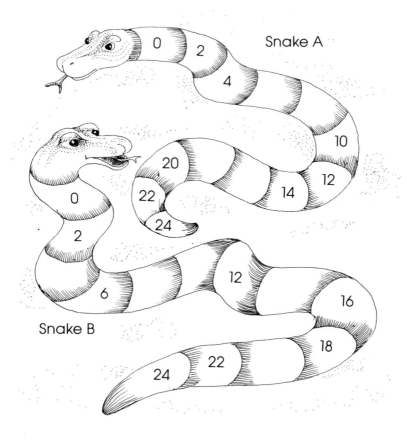

Check your answers. If you filled in the numbers correctly, go to **52**. If not, make a note of this story number and go to **40**.

Not correct! Go back to **56** if you want to find the key.

118

You should have written 'welcome to the pyramid of numbers! prepare to meet thy doom!'

If you did, the door swings open. If you did not, go back to **113** and try again. A smell of stale air hits you. It looks dark inside. Will you step in? - **122**.

119

You ask for some jewels. The Genie waves a hand, then goes back into the lamp. You see some clear jewels on the rock floor. It is quartz. This is a mineral made from sand (silica). It is not worth anything! You can rub the lamp and buy another wish from the Genie - **15** - or go on to the Pyramid - **39**.

120

You go back. You can't find a path to lead you to the Oasis. Go to **108**.

121

The shopkeeper likes all kinds of number rules. He agrees to trade. You can spare the Number Ten Bond as you know it by now! It is a fair trade. Go to **80**.

122

Well done! You've made it! You have overcome many hardships and the Pyramid awaits. You have done well and are on your way to save the Numbers of the World.

Yet more is to come! You will now have to meet the Dragon and solve many more number games. This will have to be another time. The Book of Numbers finishes here. You can go on with the next book, Number Quest. Until then, goodbye!

EQUIPMENT LIST

Adventurer, here is your Equipment List. Use it when you write down equipment you find on your journey.

If you stop reading write down the number you are on. Then you will know where to start next time.

Equipment   **Story number**